SUPPORTING PENCIL GRASP DEVELOPMENT

ACTIVITIES AND WORKSHEETS TO HELP CHILDREN DEVELOP A FUNCTIONAL PENCIL GRASP

BY

KIM GRIFFIN

First published in 2019
By GriffinOTLtd
Amersham UK

ww.GriffinOT.com

© Griffin, Kim.

Supporting Pencil Grasp Development. Activities and Worksheets to Help Children Develop a Functional Pencil Grasp.

First Edition.

ISBN: 978-1-9164691-1-2

Printed by Book Printing UK
Remus House, Coltsfoot Drive, Peterborough, PE2 9BF

Contents

About GriffinOT

Griffin Occupational Therapy provides affordable online children's occupational therapy (OT) solutions for schools and families. Our packages are designed to help teachers and parents understand and support their children's sensory processing and/or motor skill challenges. This includes, but is not limited to, children of all ages who may have sensory issues, motor skill or developmental delays, autism, or ADHD. Whilst we wholeheartedly believe that direct OT intervention is best practice, we are aware that in many cases there can be limited access to occupational therapists. GriffinOT online training and programmes can be used alongside direct OT provision and as standalone training.

GriffinOT launched our first online Sensory Processing Disorder training in the UK in October 2017. This course, *Sensory Processing – What's the Fuss?*, provides an introduction to Sensory Processing Disorder (SPD) for parents and teachers. It was followed by our first book, *Sensory Group Book 1*, in 2018. In early 2019, we launched a free in introductory Sensory Processing Disorder training.

Supporting Pencil Grasp Development is our second book. It is one part of our fine motor skill development programme. This online programme provides targeted activities to develop children's fine motor skills. In addition to the pencil grip development programme, there are four levels of developmentally sequenced fine motor activities. Each level of the programme includes a minimum of 30 activities designed to help to improve children's fine motor skills. There are clear instructional videos for each activity. Additionally, there are educational videos describing each skill that is being developed. You can find more details about these programmes on page 64.

All of our programmes are written by paediatric occupational therapist Kim Griffin. Kim has more than 15 years' experience of working with children with sensory-processing challenges and motor skill challenges. Kim has worked in Australia, Ireland and the UK. She hopes that the GriffinOT online training and resources provide clear occupational therapy programme guidance for both parents and teaching staff. Kim's aim is to do more than just give you a list of activities. She wants to ensure you know why you are doing those activities and, most importantly, how to do them safely and correctly.

To learn more about GriffinOT you can visit our website www.GriffinOT.com, join our mailing list or follow us on social media.

Facebook: www.facebook.com/GriffinSensoryOT/

Twitter: @Griffin_OT

Introduction

What is Supporting Pencil Grasp Development all about?

Supporting Pencil Grasp Development is a programme of activities and worksheets designed to help to develop a child's pencil grasp and pencil control. It can be used with an individual child, with a small group or as a whole class intervention.

The programme consists of:

- Warm-up song – *Crocodile Snap*
- Fine motor activities designed to help with finger isolation and control required to develop a functional pencil grasp
- Over 400 pencil control development worksheets, which are broken into different levels of difficulty.

Goals of the programme

1. The child will use a functional pencil grasp, see page 14 for details, when using a pencil to colour, draw and write.
2. The child will hold the paper with their non-dominant hand when they are colouring, drawing or writing.
3. The child will be able to complete the following pre-writing shapes or letters:
   a. 4 year olds – | – o +
   b. 5 year olds – above shapes plus □ \ /
   c. 6 year olds – above shapes plus x Δ and 60% of the letters of the alphabet
   d. 7+ year olds – above plus all letters of the alphabet.
4. The child will be able to complete worksheets containing multiple curves with 80% accuracy:
   a. 4 year olds – 2cm thick mazes
   b. 5 year olds – 1cm thick mazes
   c. 6 year olds – 0.5cm thick lines
   d. 7+ year olds – 0.2cm dotted lines.

Which children is the programme suitable for?

✓ Children from 3 ½ years of age that are developing their pencil grasp and control

✓ All children aged 4-8

✓ Any child that has a poorly developed pencil grasp or holds their pencil awkwardly for their age

✓ Any child that has poor pencil control for their age

Are there any children that would not be suitable for the programme?

The programme is designed for children that have an interest in colouring and mark making. For children who are not already picking up a pencil and engaging in mark making, the activities will likely be too advanced. Level one or two of the GriffinOT fine motor skill development programme is recommended for these children before they begin this pencil grasp development programme. You can find the details on these programmes on page 64 and within the additional online materials.

Who can run the programme?

The programme is designed to be used by teaching staff, including teachers and teaching support staff. It can also be used by parents at home. Adults running the programme are responsible for providing adequate supervision during the activities and adhering to the activity instructions and tips at all times.

How frequently do the activities need to be completed?

Each activity or worksheet takes approximately five minutes to complete. It is recommended that between two to five activities are completed each session. Ideally sessions should be completed a minimum of three times a week. Activities and worksheets could also be included daily before writing sessions at school or home.

It is essential that the child is reminded to use their *crocodile fingers* (see page 25) at any point when they are using writing instruments (e.g. crayons, markers, pencils). Crocodile fingers can also be encouraged when the child is using a paint brush.

Pencil Grasp Development

This chapter outlines how a child's grasp develops prior to them being ready to hold a pencil. It describes the developmental stages that lead to functional pencil grasp. The chapter also considers commonly seen pencil grasps, both the functional and non-functional ones.

There is additional video material available on our website for this chapter demonstrating examples of all of the grasps described. As a tip, we would highly recommend that you watch the video alongside reading this chapter. For more details please see page 63.

Stages before pencil grasp

Grasp reflex

When they are born, babies have what is called a 'grasp or palmer reflex.' This causes their fingers to close when you touch their palm. This movement is a reflex and it is not something that they have any functional control over. It usually disappears between 2-4 months as the child starts to develop more control over their hands and fingers.

One this happens, the child does not automatically have the ability to grasp objects. Firstly, they will reach towards objects and swipe or move their arm back and forth. This is because a child's motor skills develop in what is called a 'proximodistal' manner. This means that their larger arm movements develop before their finger control develops. To start with, a child can move their shoulder, which causes their hand to move but they don't have good control over their hand or fingers yet. As their control develops a child will be able to hold onto an item. When they do this they will use a palmer grasp.

Palmer grasp

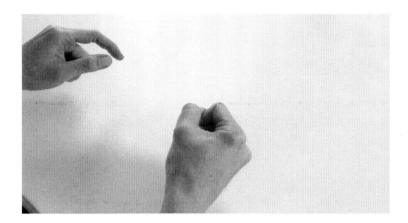

A palmer grasp is the first grasp the child has active control over. They hold the object in their whole hand as shown in the picture. The object will make contact with their palm; this is why it is called a palmer grasp. It is also sometimes called a gross grasp. The palmer grasp usually emerges by six months of age.

Forefinger grasp

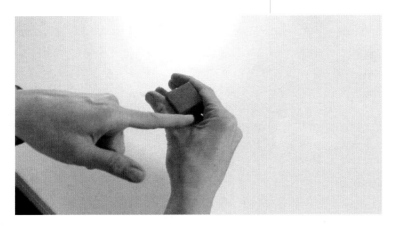

As the child has more experience holding onto items, their hand control will improve. They will develop a forefinger grasp. This looks similar to palmer grasp, but instead of the item making contact with their palm it is secured in their fingers. This is an important developmental step with regards to hand control as it is the start of having more control over the fingers.

Radial digital grasp

By ten months a child has usually developed a radial digital grasp. This means the child holds the item with their fingers on the thumb side of their hand. It is called radial digital as the bone on the thumb side of the arm is called the radius and the Latin for fingers is *digitos*. When this grasp has matured a child will be able to hold an item within the bottom half of primarily their thumb, index and middle fingers. This helps to prepare the child to hold items in their finger-tips.

Finger isolation

Finger isolation is the ability to move each finger by itself. So the thumb, index finger, middle, ring and little finger can all move independently of each other. Whilst it's not something that a child would pay much attention to day to day, it is occurring functionally all of the time. To establish a functional pencil grasp, the child must isolate their thumb, index and middle fingers from the other fingers of their hand. They must also be able to tuck their little and ring fingers out of the way. Finger isolation begins with isolation of the index finger to poke and point. This skill develops around 9 months of age.

Pincer grasp

The next grasp that a child develops is the pincer grasp. This is where they can hold a small item, e.g. a raisin, in between the pads of their thumb and index finger. It develops after the child can isolate their index finger by pointing. Before they are able to easily pick up a small item using a controlled pincer grasp, the child will start to what is called 'rake' items. This is where they are using their fingers to try to get the item by raking their fingers back and forth to try to secure the item. Next they will use an inferior pincer grasp where they hold the item more on the side of their finger rather than on the pads. And with practice they will finally develop a mature pincer grasp. A child's pincer grasp is usually fully developed around their first birthday.

Lateral grasp

The final grasp that is worth mentioning is a lateral grasp. This is where a child secures an item using the pad of their thumb and the side of their index finger. It is the grasp that you would use on a key when opening the door. It is not a grasp that is used very often functionally as once the thumb is secured against the side of the hand there are limited movements that the fingers can make. The hand can only move by turning from the forearm, as you do when you lock or unlock a door. There is some wrist movement available but other than that the movement your hand can do is quite limited. Some children use a lateral grasp during activities when they should be using a three finger grasp or pincer grasp. This means they have less control over the movement their fingers make.

Release

The other skill that emerges alongside grasping is release, or letting go of an object. Initially this happens by accident or when the child has become tired from holding on. As their grasp and control develop they can then release an item to a specific space (e.g. putting a toy into your hand). Eventually, by around 12 months or their first birthday, they can deliberately drop an item in to a smaller space (e.g. a bowl).

After the child has turned one, they develop even more control over their hands and fingers. They start to build, shake, twist, put things together and eventually pick up a pen. They start to feed themselves and take off their clothes. Their use of both hands together improves and they will eventually develop hand dominance and use a pencil. All of this develops from the primitive grasp reflex!

Hand dominance

Establishing hand dominance is one of those skills that ticks off quite a significant developmental milestone. For children who are slow to choose their dominant hand it can cause worry and sometimes frustration for parents and educators.

Hand dominance is said to develop between two-half to six years of age, depending on the author. Mary Sheridan (2008, p.36) suggests that at two and a half years of age 'children will hold a pen in their preferred hand.' Keith Beery (2010, p.116) suggests that it isn't until 5 years and 6 months that a child would prefer to use either their right or left hand. These are useful ballpark figures, but all children are different. Some will have an obvious preferred hand very early on at age four, whereas others do take that bit longer.

If a child isn't showing some signs of hand preference by the age of five, they may need further assessment by an occupational therapist. This is especially true if the child is not crossing midline with their hands at age five. Midline is that imaginary line that runs down our body. Crossing midline means that you use your right hand on the left side or your body and your left hand on your right side. A child that doesn't cross midline will only use their right hand on the right side and then switch to their left hand on the left side. So if they draw a cross (+) they might draw the left side of the horizontal line with their left hand and then the right side of the horizontal line with their right hand. If you observe this with a child who is age five or older it is recommended that you seek out additional occupational therapy assessment and intervention.

What is less concerning is if a child swaps hands more when they become tired, something that can occur more frequently in children with low tone and hypermobility. These children will do the activity for a bit, crossing midline and then they will change hands but they will also cross midline with this hand as well. This is different to the children that swap hands when they need to cross midline.

If hand dominance isn't established by aged six it is again suggested that you seek out additional assessment and advice from an occupational therapist.

If you are not sure of a child's dominance and they are five years or older and do not have a neurological condition or significant developmental delays, watch them for a week. Which hand do they use to open a door? Which hand do they use to hold their spoon and toothbrush and to pull up their zip? What about during play, which hand do they most commonly reach for things with? When they ask for a sweet, which hand do they produce to receive it? If you can keep a record of how many times they used their left or right hand you might see a preference. Don't just look at how they hold a pencil. You can also check which foot they use by asking them to kick a ball and also which eye they would firstly look through a kaleidoscope (or telescope made out of an old kitchen roll) as this might also give you some more clues about which side of their body is becoming more dominant.

If they are pretty much 50/50 and the telescope ends up in the middle of their eyes, then they really haven't established hand dominance yet. If they are six years or older, as noted above, additional assessment is recommended. If there is more of a pattern towards one side (e.g. 75% of the time they use their left) then it is more likely this is their dominant hand. You could encourage that side for pencil skills.

Stages of pencil grasp development

Again, there is additional video material available on our website for this section demonstrating examples of all of the grasps described. As a tip, we would highly recommend that you watch the video alongside reading this section. For more details please see page 63.

Pencil grasp develops in a sequence as a child's hand grasps and fine motor skills develop. It develops in a proximodistal manner, starting with the whole hand and moving out to the fingers. To be efficient with their pencil skills, the child also needs to be able to hold the paper steady, so their non-dominant hand is doing something different to their dominant hand.

Gross or palmer grasp

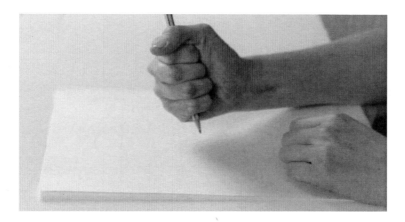

Initially the child will use what is called a gross grasp or a palmer grasp. The pencil will be secured in their fingers and palm. The movement usually will come from the shoulder or elbow, but there may also be some wrist movement. This is typical for a 12-18 month year old, but immature after this age. When using this grasp the child can only mark larger pencil movements. The will have limited precision.

Digital pronate grasp

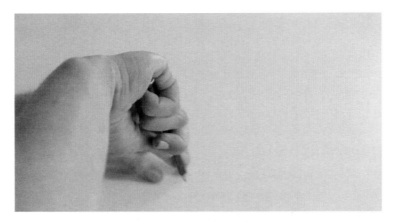

Between 2-3 years of age a child will start to use what is called a 'digital pronate grasp'. Let's break that down. *Digital* refers to the fingers, meaning the child is no longer holding the pencil in their fist or palm. *Pronate* means to turn the thumb to the floor. It is the name of the movement that our forearm makes when the palm turns down to the floor. So the child holds the pencil in their fingers with their palm turned around so their little finger faces the ceiling. This is similar to the progression from a palmer grasp to a radial digital grasp, the control moves from the palm out towards the fingers. The reason the child turns their hand to the floor, however, is that they just don't have the shoulder stability, elbow, wrist or finger control required to hold the pencil and make marks by just moving their fingers and wrist. This grasp reduces the precision children have over with their pencil movements.

Static tripod

Around the age of 3 ½ to 4 years old the child will turn their hand over and start with a static tripod grasp. This is where the pencil is held in between the tips of the thumb, index and middle finger. The child however controls the pencil movement from their wrist and elbow. It is called a 'static' tripod because the fingers remain still or static.

Dynamic tripod

In a dynamic tripod grasp the pencil remains held in between the tips of the thumb, index and middle finger, as shown above. The index finger should be controlling the movement and the thumb and middle finger help with directional control. There will be a nice open web-space. There should be good movement at the fingers, rather than the wrist controlling the movement. This is what separates a dynamic tripod or moving tripod from its less mature static tripod or still tripod. The fingers are in the same position for both grasps, but when a child has developed dynamic control their fingers control the movement, not their wrist. Children will develop this control somewhere between the ages of four to six years of age.

The reason the dynamic tripod is championed is because it provides the most amount of pencil control for the least amount of muscle effort. This helps to facilitate speed of writing. In reality however, it is common to see a variation of this grasp in adults, or for some people something that looks nothing like this grasp!

The reason so much focus is put onto pencil grasp, in my opinion, is that it is because the other grasps are less efficient. If you're controlling your pencil from your wrist, or elbow, or shoulder in some cases, then you are using more effort so you will tire more quickly. You also have less finger movement and control. If you have your thumb wrapped around your fingers, you again have less finger movement, which will reduce your speed and also make you tire more quickly. If you are really squeezing your pencil with your hand or fingers you will definitely tire more quickly and also typically end up with a sore hand very quickly. This is why the tripod grasp holds the top place.

Pencil Grasps – What's Functional?

Functional and mature pencil grasps

There is additional video material available on our website for this chapter demonstrating examples of all of the grasps described. As a tip, we would highly recommend that you watch the video alongside reading this chapter. For more details please see page 63.

Tripods – dynamic

Most text books suggest that the optimal pencil grasp is what is called a dynamic tripod grasp. The dynamic tripod grasp, as mentioned earlier, is when a child holds their pencil with their index and middle fingers and thumb. The pencil movement should come from the fingers, resulting in dynamic control or a dynamic tripod.

Quadruped – dynamic

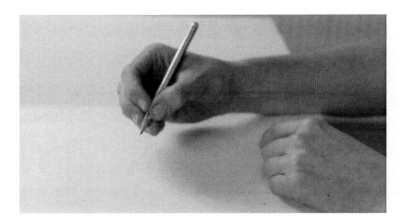

There is research which shows that a dynamic quadruped grasp is as effective as a dynamic tripod grasp. In a quadruped grasp the child holds the pencil with their thumb, index, middle and ring fingers on the pencil, with the little finger tucked away. It is important that the child is still holding the pencil with the tips of their fingers, rather than their thumb being wrapped around. By the age of seven, the pencil movement should also come from the fingers rather than the wrist. So, if you're seeing this grip, mark it as mature.

Middle finger control

You may also see children with a tripod or quadruped grasp that control the pencil with their middle finger. Usually this is ok, as long as they have kept their web-space open and the movement is coming from their fingers.

Modified or alternative tripod

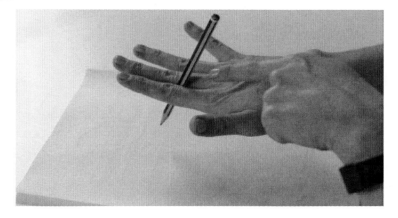

Another grasp that is less well known but highly effective for the children who can adapt to it, is the modified or alternative tripod grasp. For this grasp the child needs to put the pencil between their index and middle fingers and then curl these fingers and their thumb around onto the pencil. This feels very strange when you first try it. However, it takes the weight of the pencil, so for children with low tone it can be a good option. It also secures the pencil, so, if you let go the pencil, for the most part, stays in place. Whilst this grip does look and feel quite strange, it is a good alternative as it means the child can use it on any pen or pencil, rather than needing to remember and or find a pencil grip. It can also be particularly effective for children who use a thumb wrap grasp if they are able to change to it.

Grasps that are less functional

The pencil grasp of children with poor fine motor skills is often delayed. Frequently, these children will find an alternative way to hold onto their pencil. This is frequently because they don't have the shoulder stability, finger isolation or maturity in their hand grasps when they first start to use a pencil. So, they develop a pencil grasp that they can manage. The reason these grasps are not ideal is because they don't allow for optimal finger movement and control of the pencil.

Some common less functional grasps you might see are as follows:

Fingers along shaft

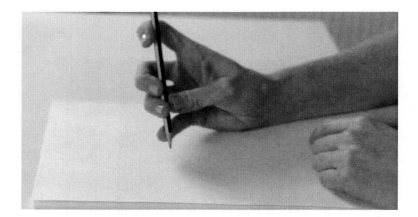

The child spreads all of their fingers along the shaft of the pencil and controls the pencil with their little finger. The child may also hook their index finger right around the top of the pencil. This grasp is frequently seen in children with low tone and hypermobility. It is likely that this is because it is easier for them to keep a hold of the pencil but it gives them more control than a digital pronate grasp. It is not a very functional grasp though, as the child will never develop dynamic control of their fingers. Therefore, it reduces their pencil control and limits their writing speed in the long term.

Thumb wrap

The second very common grasp is a thumb wrap. This is where the child starts off with a tripod but their thumb quickly wraps around their pencil and fingers. You may also see a thumb tuck, where the child tucks their thumb in, under their fingers instead of wrapping it over the top. Usually this happens because children require more feedback about what their hand is doing, or they don't have the finger strength to hold the pencil easily in their fingertips. Children using this grasp may complain of pain in the hand when writing for longer periods as they typically use more effort to control their pencil.

Lateral grasp

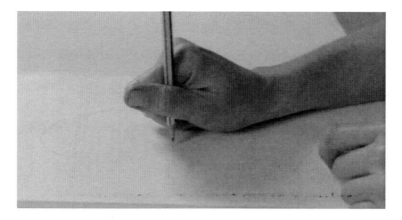

Children might also use a more lateral grasp on their pencil. This means they will secure it along the side of their index finger, wrap their thumb around and control the movement by squeezing their hand, rather than moving their fingers at the joints. This grip, again, allows for very limited dynamic movement.

To pencil grip, or not to pencil grip?

No pencil grasp book would be complete without a discussion on pencil grips. In this book the term pencil grip will be used to indicate a moulded grip that has been put onto the pencil. Whereas pencil grasp has and will be used to indicate the position that the children's fingers are on the pencil.

My advice for children that are under five, and sometimes, if they have developmental delays, under six years old, is to look at writing utensils that will help to support their finger and hand development first before giving them a pencil grip. If you have a child who is still holding onto their pencil with their whole hand, so a gross pencil grasp, this means that their hand and finger skills just haven't developed enough to hold onto their pencil with their fingers. These children need more support to develop their hand and finger control.

The first thing that is helpful is to use finger crayons. These are designed for two to three year olds but are great to get children holding onto a writing implement with their fingers! They are also good because they are round at the top, so it also helps to develop the arches of the hand. You will find further information on using these crayons in the worksheets chapter (page 40).

Secondly, the programme suggests using small pencils. These can be made by sawing regular thick pencils into 3-4cm lengths (see page 40 for an example). This is a great strategy for children that still hold onto the whole pencil shaft as it forces the child to use their fingers as they can't hold onto the pencil with their whole hand as it's not big enough. You can do the same with small pieces of crayon as well. It is important to make sure the child is holding onto this with their finger-tips, and not with a lateral grasp. If this is occurring, they may need more help to support their fine motor skill development.

If the child is holding the pencil with their fingers but their grasp is not mature, you can firstly try the quadruped and alternate tripod grasp. These were discussed in the previous chapter 'functional pencil grasps.'

For children who have started to hold the pencil with their fingers, rather than their whole hand, but who are still struggling to get the correct fingers onto their pencil, there is one grip that can help in the majority of cases. This is the grotto grip.

As the pencil grip market is so saturated and there are new grips arriving each month, it is difficult to provide an up-to-date list of pencil grips. In order to keep recommendations current, review videos are posted on the GriffinOT social media channels. You will find further information on this on page 63.

The final piece of advice is, it's really tricky to change a child's pencil grasp after the age of seven, unless THEY are very motivated to do so. Whilst there is not a specific reference to support this observation it is what I have seen clinically as an occupational therapist. In summary, the earlier children can be supported to develop their pencil grasp, the easier it will be for them to develop a functional grasp.

Running the Programme

Materials needed

The full set of resources is below. These are listed again with each activity. All of the resources are commercially available. It is likely you will have most of them already.

- Table and chair to work at
- Small pieces of dowel or counters, coins or pieces of sponge
- Resistance band (e.g. Theraband®)
- Duplo, OR, for older children – Lego
- Playdough
- Coins and a money box
- Building blocks
- Small sponges (can be made by cutting up a regular kitchen sponge)
- Water Magic books OR paint and paper
- Beads and string (for threading, use a size the child can thread easily)
- Small plastic containers or bowls (to transfer water into) – preferably 2 per child
- Coloured paper (and optional paper and glue)
- Medicine droppers (plastic)
- Finger crayons (see page 40)
- Small 3-4cm pencils (see page 40 for details)
- Regular pencils
- Markers
- Internet access and printer to print worksheets
- Balloons – 3 per child
- Rice or playdough to put into the balloons – enough to fill 1 balloon per child

Before you start – set up

It is recommended the following is completed prior to starting the programme:

- Decide on when the programme will be timetabled into the week and who will be running it
- Once you have identified the amount of time you have for the programme, decide on how many activities you will complete each session and make a rough plan to follow. Allow yourself some flexibility as different children may need more time on some activities
- Source the materials required for the programme – most you should have either in your classroom or at home
- If required, print out an initial-assessment form for each child and complete it
- If required, print out copies of the session record sheet.

Please note that printable formats for all documents can be downloaded from the GriffinOT website, please see page 63 for details.

Before you start – child assessment

Before starting the programme, you can complete the pre-assessment. It is available on page 60 and can be downloaded from our website, see page 63 for details. The pre-assessment helps to track the child's improvements. If you are already recording this within your own recording systems, you may not need to record it again.

How long should we spend on each activity?

Each activity should take approximately five minutes. It is recommended that the activities are completed at least three times before the child moves onto the next activity, however some children may need more practice to be successful. There is a suggested final target given for each activity. If the child has not met this target after three times, they should continue practising the activity until they can reach the target.

It is recommended the worksheets are completed until the child meets the 'accuracy goal' of 80%. For easier two and four centimetre wide maze worksheets, this means that the child can complete 8/10 of the mazes without coming outside of the line. With harder worksheets (e.g. 1cm wide mazes, dotted lines) a target of 80% accuracy on each worksheet is suggested.

Older children (5+) will likely find the initial sets of worksheets too easy. They can start with harder worksheets, rather than needing to start at level 1. The child's level of ability can be checked by using the worksheet assessment packs, which are available within the additional online materials (see page 63).

How many activities should we do each time?

This will depend on the amount of time you have available and the number of children you are working with. The programme allows you to be flexible. You may wish to use the activities and worksheets as a formal lesson or group. You may also wish to use them as part of your own lesson plan. It is highly recommended that you spend time on both the worksheets and the activities each week, rather than just focusing on one.

Example 1 – Using the programme with an individual

Jon's mum is running the programme with him at home. She has set aside 20 minutes three times a week. During each session Jon's mum plans to do both warm-ups, one activity and 3 pencil worksheets. This means Jon's first two weeks will look like this:

Week 1 – Monday, Wednesday, Saturday

- Warm-up 1
- Warm-up 2
- Activity 1
- Worksheets Level 1 (3-4 sheets)

Week 2 – Monday, Wednesday, Saturday

- Warm-up 1
- Warm-up 2
- Activity 2
- Worksheets Level 1 (3-4 sheets).

Example 2 – Using the programme with a small group

Tara, a teaching assistant, is running the programme with a group of five children at her school. She has 25 minutes to work with the children three times a week. Her sample group schedule would look like this:

Week 1 – Monday, Tuesday, Thursday

- Warm-up 1 – 10 minutes allocated to practice song
- Activity 1
- Activity 2
- Worksheets level 1 (3-4 sheets each)

Week 2 – Monday, Tuesday, Thursday

- Warm-up 1
- Warm-up 2
- Activity 2
- Activity 3
- Worksheets level 2 (3-4 sheets each).

Example 3 – Using the programme with a class

Dave has decided to use the programme with his whole class, they are a bit older, so he plans to start at level 4 with the worksheets. He plans to integrate the activities and worksheets into his handwriting lesson time. He will alternate the warm-ups each week. His plan looks like this:

Week 1 – Daily

- Warm-up 1
- Activity 1
- Worksheets level 4 (2 sheets each)
- Continue with handwriting lesson as planned

Week 2 – Daily

- Warm-up 2
- Activity 2
- Worksheets level 4 (2 sheets each)
- Continue with handwriting lesson as planned.

As you go along – recording progress

There is an activity record sheet (page 62) for recording the performance of children on the activities and worksheets if you require a more formal way to record the information each time you complete them. As noted above, you may already be recording this information using your own format and if this is working please don't feel like you need to record the information twice.

When you finish – measuring outcomes

There is a Pre- and Review Assessment form (page 60). This allows you to document the child's progress with their pencil grasp and also their pencil control.

In addition to written recording, a video or picture record of the child's pencil grasp can be a great way to show their improvement. Periodic examples of their worksheets, drawings and writing can also be kept for comparison to show improvements.

Warm-ups

Crocodile Snap

Words by Kim Griffin, Music by Pat Savina. Please see the additional online materials (page 63) for links to the music and action video for the song.

Fingers can wiggle, wiggle, wiggle, wiggle,   (Wiggle fingers)
Fingers can snap, snap, snap, snap.   (Open and close fingers to thumb, like a crocodile mouth)
Fingers can wiggle, wiggle, wiggle, wiggle,   (Wiggle fingers)
Hands can clap, clap, clap, clap.   (Clap hands)
Let's go and find your writing hand
Thumb can wiggle,   (Wiggle and snap each finger separately)
Thumb can snap;
Peter can wiggle,
Peter can snap;
Toby can wiggle,
Toby can snap;
Ruby can wiggle,
Ruby can snap;
Even baby can wiggle,
And baby can snap;
Everybody wiggle,
Everybody snap.
Now let's try the other hand out (Repeat verse)

Now what does this all mean?
Fingers can wiggle, wiggle, wiggle, wiggle,
Fingers can snap, snap, snap, snap.
Fingers can freeze;
Hold it still!
Bye bye baby,   (Tuck little finger into palm)
Bye bye ring,   (Tuck ring finger into palm)
It's time to let our crocodiles sing;   (Open and close index and middle finger to thumb)
Ready crocodiles!
We hold your pencil,
We're ready to write,
We'll help you colour,
With all our might,
We'll work super hard,
We will not nap,
But just remember,
Crocodiles can snap!

Snap your ear,   (Snap right ear)
Snap your nose,   (Snap nose)
Snap your shoulder.   (Snap left shoulder)
Snap them fast,
Snap them slow,
Snap them over.   (Make an arc from right to left, left to right)

Resistance ball

Please see the additional online materials (page 63) for a video demonstrating how to make your own resistance ball. It is essential that these are not put into a child's mouth, so they should only be used with children who will not mouth them.

The aim with the resistance ball is to squeeze and release it with your crocodile fingers. So, using the index and middle finger and the thumb the children should squeeze, or pinch, and release the ball. Continue to this movement on the ball for 3-5 minutes.

The ball should not be touching their palm. The squeeze movement should be coming from the fingers only, rather than the child's whole hand.

Children with more control can pinch or squeeze the ball with their thumb and index finger. Then they can use their thumb and middle finger, then their thumb and ring finger and their thumb and little finger. Again, ensure that they are not touching the ball to their palm.

Activities

There are two types of activities within this programme.

Crocodile fingers

The first provides opportunities for the child to use their *crocodile fingers*. When doing these activities it is recommended that you refer back to the song, *Crocodile Snap*, to prompt the children to use their *crocodile fingers.* For each activity you are aiming for the child to tuck their little and ring fingers away and to just use their thumb, index finger and middle finger to do the activity. If the child is struggling to do this you can also use the dowel as described below to help them to stabilise.

Stabilising - dowel

The second set of activities allows the children to continue to practice keeping their little and ring fingers tucked away. These are called stabilising activities. What you will need for these activities is a small piece of dowel, a coin or a round marker that the child can hold onto. The aim is that they hold onto this item with their little and ring fingers and they use their thumb index and middle fingers to complete the activity. Throughout the activity descriptions this item will be called the dowel. You will need two of these per child.

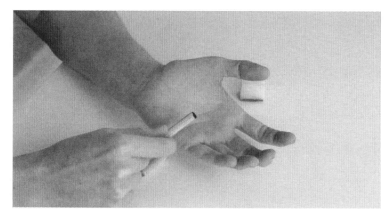

Activity PG1:   Crocodile fingers – pull band with an adult

What you need   1 piece of resistance band cut into 30cm length for each adult

Final target   The child can pull the band forward 10 times slowly using just their thumb, index and middle fingers.

What to do

Adult's hand

✓ The adult holds the band and the child then takes the end with their *crocodile fingers* (see page 25).
✓ The child then pulls the band forward (like a tug of war) using these fingers, releasing the tension off and then pulling again.
✓ Swap to the other hand and repeat.

Other tips

- Children will often let go of the band so that it flings forward and snaps. In this case, count "1 2 3 pull", "3 2 1 stop" and teach the child how to move their hand forward to release the tension.
- Children will also try to grab the band with their whole hand. Remind them to use their *crocodile fingers*.
- Match the level of resistance to the hand strength of the child. All bands come in different resistance strengths (and each brand has its own colour system, making it hard to recommend a colour). Younger children or children with less hand strength will need a lower resistance band and older children may require a middle level of resistance.

Activity PG2:   Stabilising and Duplo

What you need   Duplo (for older children Lego is ok)

Item you are using to stabilise with e.g. dowel – 2 per child

Final target   The child can build a tower to 10 bricks whilst stabilising an item in their dominant hand. For children aged 5+ they will, ideally, be able to stabilise an item in both hands.

What to do

- ✓ Secure the dowel as described on page 25 into the child's dominant hand.
- ✓ Allow the child to build and pull apart towers of Duplo or make other creations for 2 minutes.
- ✓ Swap the dowel into their other hand and continue for a further 2 minutes.
- ✓ Then try to build with the dowel in both hands for a minute or two.

Other tips

- Prompt the child to keep hold of the dowel, slow the activity down if they can't manage and give clear instructions on what to build e.g. a tower with a blue, red and green brick.
- If the child is really struggling with their dominant hand, practice this hand for longer and don't do both hands.
- If the child achieves the activity easily with one hand, spend all of the time completing the activity with the dowel secured in both hands.

Activity PG3:   Crocodile fingers – taking playdough

What you need   Playdough – 1 container per adult

Final target   The child can pull off 10 pieces of playdough using just their thumb, index and middle fingers.

What to do

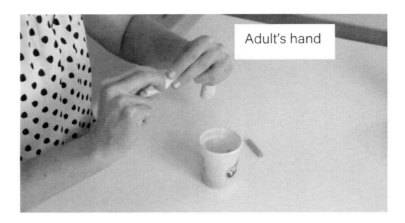

Adult's hand

✓ The adult rolls the playdough into a snake.
✓ The child needs to take off (snap) small pieces of dough with their *crocodile fingers* (see page 25).
✓ The child should hold the container with their other hand and place the pieces of dough into it.
✓ Then swap hands and do the activity with their other hand.

Other tips

• Encourage the child to take the dough with their finger-tips.
• Children will also try to grab the dough with their whole hand. Remind them to use their *crocodile fingers*. You may need to physically help them to tuck their little and ring fingers away.
• Encourage the child to hold the container with their other hand. This helps them to improve their ability to use both hands together, like they need to do when stabilising their paper for writing.

Activity PG4:   Stabilising and posting coins

What you need   Money box
Coins or counters
Item you are using to stabilise with e.g. dowel – 2 per child

Final target   The child can post 10 coins whilst stabilising an item in their dominant hand.

What to do

✓ Secure the dowel as described on page 25 into the child's dominant hand.
✓ Have the child hold the box with the other hand.
✓ Then post the coins into the box.
✓ Then complete the activity with the dowel in their other hand (the hand with the dowel is always the one posting the coins into the box).

Other tips

- If you are using a marker or coin as your item to stabilise make sure this is a different colour or a different coin to the ones you are using for the activity. So, the child can easily see if they have dropped the one they are meant to be stabilising.
- Prompt the child to keep hold of the dowel, slow the activity down if they can't manage, and reduce the number of coins.
- If the child achieves the activity easily you can increase the number of coins and also time them.

Activity PG5:   Crocodile fingers – build towers

What you need   2-5cm big cube blocks
You can also use wooden beads if you don't have blocks, stacking containers will also work

Final target   The child can make a tower of 8 bricks using just their thumb, index and middle fingers.

What to do

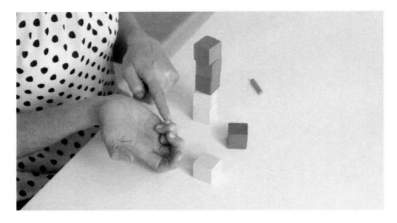

✓ Encourage the child to build their tower using just with their *crocodile fingers* (see page 25) on the bricks.

Other tips

• If the child is struggling to do this independently the adult can hold the brick up and have the child take it from them using the correct fingers. It can sometimes be easier to take the brick from a forward position.
• You can also use the dowel to help if needed, as shown in the picture.

Activity PG6:   Stabilising and sponge painting

What you need   2cm cube shaped pieces of sponge (made by cutting up a kitchen sponge)
Water Magic and water OR
Paint and paper
Item you are using to stabilise with e.g. dowel – 2 per child

Final target   The child can paint for five minutes whilst stabilising an item in their dominant hand.

What to do

- ✓ Secure the dowel as described on page 25 into the child's dominant hand.
- ✓ The child then paints with the sponge until the pictures are shown. Or if they are using paint, they can paint until their paper is covered with dots of paint.

Other tips

- Prompt the child to keep hold of the dowel.
- Encourage the child to hold the paper with their non-dominant hand. This hand can also hold a dowel if the child is ready for an extra challenge.

Activity PG7:   Crocodile fingers – pull band by self

What you need   Resistance band cut into 15cm length – 1 for each child

Final target   The child can pull the band apart 20 times slowly using just their thumb, index and middle fingers.

What to do

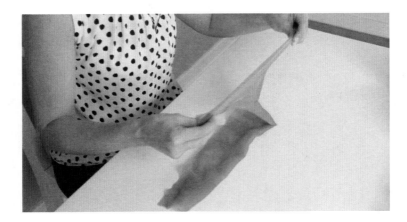

✓ The child needs to hold each side of the band with their thumb, index and middle fingers.
✓ They then pull the band apart using these fingers.
✓ This can be done in time with a song or metronome to create a rhythm.

Other tips

• Match the level of resistance to the hand strength of the child. All bands come in different resistance strengths (and each brand has its own colour system, making it hard to recommend a colour). Younger children or children with less hand strength will need a lower resistance band and older children may require a middle level of resistance.
• Children will also try to grab the band with their whole hand. Remind them to use their *crocodile fingers.*

Activity PG8: Stabilising and threading

What you need   Beads and string – choose a size that the child can easily thread

Item you are using to stabilise with e.g. dowel – 2 per child

Final target   The child can thread 15 beads whilst stabilising an item in their dominant hand.

For children aged 5+ they will ideally be able to stabilise and item in both hands.

What to do

- ✓ Secure the dowel as described on page 25 into the child's dominant hand.
- ✓ Have the child thread beads for 2 minutes.
- ✓ Swap the dowel into their other hand and continue for a further 2 minutes.
- ✓ Then try to complete the activity with the dowel in both hands, as demonstrated in the picture, for a minute or two.

Other tips

- Make sure the child can easily thread the beads you choose when they are not holding the dowel. The focus of this activity is finger isolation rather than threading. If they need larger sized beads to be successful this is ok.
- Prompt the child to keep hold of the dowel, slow the activity down if they can't manage.
- If the child is really struggling with their dominant hand practice this for longer and don't do both hands.
- If the child achieves the activity easily with one hand, spend all of the time completing the activity with the dowel secured in both hands.
- You can also use smaller beads if the child is able to easily thread with these.
- If they find beads too easy you can also use lacing cards.

Activity PG9:   Crocodile fingers – squeeze sponges

What you need   2cm cube shaped pieces of sponge (made by cutting up a kitchen sponge)
Container with water – ideally with food colouring
Empty container – ideally clear

Final target   The child will be able to transfer water with sponges using just their thumb, index and middle fingers.

What to do

✓ The child holds the sponge with their *crocodile fingers* (see page 25).
✓ They dip the sponge into the water and then move over to the empty container and squeeze the water into this.
✓ Continue for at least 10 squeezes with their dominant hand.
✓ Swap to their non-dominant hand.

Other tips

• Children will also try to squeeze the sponge with their whole hand, remind them to use their *crocodile fingers.*
• Again ensure the child is holding the first container (i.e. the one with the water to begin with) with their other hand.
• You can also put a mark onto the empty container to encourage the child to fill up to this mark if they are reluctant to persist.
• To make it harder you can put more space between the containers so the child needs to move to the second container.
• For an additional challenge you could have the child hold the first container up in the air so they have to hold this throughout the task (and not spill any water).

Activity PG10: Stabilising and rolling playdough cylinders

What you need Playdough – ¼ container per child
Item you are using to stabilise with, e.g. dowel, – 2 per child

Final target The child can roll a cylinder with their thumb, index and middle fingers whilst stabilising an item in their dominant hand. For children aged 6+ they will, ideally, be able to complete the activity holding a piece of dowel with their non-dominant hand as well.

What to do

✓ Secure the dowel as described on page 25 into the child's dominant hand.
✓ Put a small piece of playdough into the child's thumb, index and middle fingers and have them roll it backwards and forwards until it turns into a cylinder.
✓ Swap the dowel into their other hand and make another one.
✓ Continue making cylinders for 5 minutes.

Other tips

● Prompt the child to keep hold of the dowel, slow the activity down if they can't manage.
● Once the child achieves the activity easily holding dowel with one hand they can try with dowel in both hands at the same time.

Activity PG11:   Crocodile fingers – tearing paper

What you need   Coloured paper – tissue and wrapping paper works well
Glue can also be used to make a collage, but is optional

Final target   The child can tear off and roll up small (3-5 cm) pieces of paper using just their thumb, index and middle fingers.

What to do

✓ Using their *crocodile fingers* (see page 25) the children need to tear off small pieces of paper and then roll this into a ball.
✓ They can then stick this onto another piece of paper to create a collage or post it into a container.
✓ Continue for five minutes.

Other tips

• If children try to use their whole hand, remind them to use their *crocodile fingers.*
• Check that the paper you are using tears easily (some paper is trickier than others).
• If the child needs to improve their hand strength, you can tear cardboard.

Activity PG12:   Stabilising and droppers

What you need
Water droppers (large or small depending on the child)
Container with water
Container to transfer water into
Item you are using to stabilise with, e.g. dowel, – 2 per child

Final target
The child can squeeze 10 droppers full of water into the container without dropping the dowel. For children aged 6+ they will, ideally, be able to drop single drops out of the dropper rather than all of the water in one squeeze.

What to do

- ✓ Secure the dowel, as described on page 25, into the child's dominant hand.
- ✓ Have the child transfer water with the droppers from one container to the next.
- ✓ Swap the dowel into their other hand and continue for a further 2 minutes.

Other tips

- Prompt the child to keep hold of the dowel. Slow the activity down if they can't manage.
- If the child finds using the dropper too easy, you can ask them to try to drop out single drops at a time, rather than squirting all of the water out in one go.
- Again ensure the child is holding the first container (i.e. the one with the water to begin with) with their other hand.
- You can also put a mark onto the empty container to encourage the child to fill up to this mark if they are reluctant to persist.
- To make it harder you can put more space between the containers so the child needs to move to the second container.
- For an additional challenge you could have the child hold the first container up in the air so they have to hold this throughout the task (and not spill any water).

Activity PG13:   Crocodile fingers – playdough cubes

What you need   Playdough – 1/4 container per child

Final target   The child can create a cube of playdough using just their thumb, index and middle fingers.

What to do

✓ Using their *crocodile fingers* (see page 25) the child needs to squash the sides of the playdough until it becomes a cube.

✓ Children may alternate between their middle finger and thumb, index finger and thumb and both middle and index finger and thumb. This is ok as long as their little and ring fingers aren't helping.

Other tips

• This activity is really difficult so don't worry if it takes a while for the child to be able to do.

Activity PG14:   Stabilising and playdough balls

What you need   Playdough – ¼ container per child

Item you are using to stabilise with, e.g. dowel, – 2 per child

Final target   The child can roll playdough into a ball with their thumb, index and middle fingers whilst stabilising an item in their dominant hand. For children aged 6+ they will, ideally, be able to complete the activity with their non-dominant hand as well.

What to do

- ✓ Secure the dowel as described on page 25 into the child's dominant hand.
- ✓ Put a small piece of playdough into the child's thumb, index and middle fingers and have them roll it around and around until it turns into a ball (sphere).
- ✓ Swap the dowel into their other hand and make another one.
- ✓ Continue making balls for 5 minutes.

Other tips

- Prompt the child to keep hold of the dowel. Slow the activity down if they can't manage.
- This activity is also really difficult, so don't worry if it takes a while for the child to be able to do.
- Once the child achieves the activity easily with one hand, they can try to do both hands at the same time.

Worksheets

The worksheets for this programme are broken into different designs with different levels. They are designed so there will be something at the right level for each child. If you are running groups, different children could be working on different worksheet levels depending on their ability.

For all worksheets the focus must be on accuracy over speed. The programme recommends using finger crayons and short pencils with children initially to help them to develop their pencil grasp.

Finger crayons

These are commercially available from a number of different stores and also online. The shape shown in the picture is recommended over the egg shaped crayons, as these are too big for the child to hold with just their fingers.

Short pencils

Take wider pencils, these can be triangular or hexagonal, and cut them into 3cm lengths. This can be easily done with a small saw. You do not need to purchase special pencils.

Worksheets

As noted above, the worksheets for this programme are broken into different designs with different levels. This book only contains sample pictures of the worksheets. All worksheets are available to download on the GriffinOT website. Please see the details on page 63 for further information.

The worksheets start with wide mazes and progress to thin dotted lines. Each width starts with straight designs and builds up to more complex designs, including curves and corners. There are multiple pages within each set to allow children to practice without getting bored of the same sheet. The information below gives more information on the labelling system.

Mazes

All mazes are labelled mazes. They then have a number after them, example 1-1 or 4-2. The first number identifies the thickness of the maze and the second tells the shape. There are also letters, these relate to the design set, for example the letter A refers to the dinosaur illustrations. The coding system is as follows:

- Thickness
    - 1 = 4cm wide
    - 2 = 2cm wide
    - 3 = 1cm wide
    - 4 = 1cm wide combined shapes

- Shape
    - 1 = Straight
    - 2 = Slight curve
    - 3 = Diagonal
    - 4= Harder curve
    - 5 = Zig Zag

Lines

The lines are labelled lines. These start as a solid thicker line and progress to thin dotted lines. The coding system is as follows:

- Thickness
    - 1 = Solid thick line
    - 2 = Thick dotted line
    - 3 = Thin dotted line

- Shape
    - 1 = Straight and slight curve
    - 2 = Diagonals and corners
    - 3 = Multiple directions
    - 4 = Multiple directions – harder
    - 5 = Zig Zag.

Example maze worksheets:

PG Mazes 1-1A is a 4cm straight maze

PG Mazes 1-2A is a 4cm curved maze

PG Mazes 2-1A is a 2cm straight maze

PG Mazes 2-3A is a 2cm diagonal maze

Example maze worksheets:

PG Mazes 3-1A is a 1cm straight maze

PG Mazes 3-4A-is a 1cm harder curved maze

PG Mazes 3-5A is a 1cm zig zag maze

PG Mazes 4-1A is a 1cm mixed maze

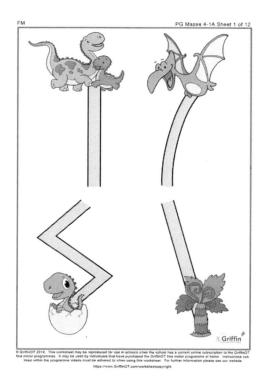

Example line worksheets:

PG Solid Lines 1-1A is a solid straight line

PG Thick Lines 2-1A is a dotted thick straight line

PG Thick Lines 2-2A is a dotted thick cornered line

PG Thin Lines 3-1A is a thin dotted straight line

Example line worksheets:

PG Thin Lines 3-3A is a thin multiple direction line   PG Thin Lines 3-4A is a thin multiple direction line

To determine which level of the worksheets to start at, you can print out and assess the child using the two packs available on the website. One pack is for younger children, the other is for older children (5+). Have the child complete the pack. The aim is that they can complete the worksheet with 80% accuracy. For the easier mazes it would be expected that 8 times out of 10 the child would stay on the path. For harder mazes and lines the aim is a total of 80% accuracy on each sheet. So, the child's pencil should stay within the boundaries or on the line for 80% of the time on the sheet. It also won't hurt if the child starts at a slightly lower level and practices this skill before moving on, especially if they are reluctant to complete worksheets. Starting at a lower level will help to give the child more confidence with their pencil skills.

Guide for worksheet activities and children's ages

It is expected that only older children will be able to complete the more difficult worksheets. Below is a general guide for children's ages and the worksheets activity they should complete.

- Three years olds – focus on the first four worksheet activities (WS1-4) and use worksheets labelled Mazes 1 & 2.
- Four year olds – focus on the first six worksheet activities (WS1-6) and use worksheets labelled Mazes 2&3 and Lines 1. These children can start at the Mazes 1 if they need to.
- Five year olds – focus on the first ten worksheet activities (WS1-10) and use worksheets labelled Mazes 3&4 and Lines 1&2. Again they can start with easier worksheets if needed.
- Over six years old – these children should be able to work through all of worksheet activities. They may be able to start immediately on worksheets labelled Mazes 4 or Lines 1. They can spend less time with finger crayons but it is recommended they use these for 2-4 weeks.

Activity WS1: Finger crayons and shape colouring

What you need Finger crayons
Worksheets – Shapes 1, 2 or 3 depending on the child's ability

Final target The child can colour in 80% of a square and circle with their strokes going out no further than 2cm of the boundary line.

What to do

✓ The child uses the finger crayons to colour in the shapes.
✓ Ensure the child is holding the crayon with their fingers.
✓ Also make sure they are holding the paper with their other hand.

Other tips

- There are three levels of worksheets here:
    - o Shapes 1 – easy shapes with few edges and turns
    - o Shapes 2 – harder shapes with many edges and turns
    - o Shapes 3 – pictures – some children with a lower level of skill may be more motivated by colouring in the pictures initially, so these can be used to facilitate engagement, even if the child cannot stay within the lines.

Activity WS2:   Finger crayons and lines

What you need   Finger crayons
Blank paper – ideally large paper

Final target   The child can draw a vertical and horizontal line and attempt a circle.

What to do

- ✓ Using the finger crayons the child needs to copy the shapes as they are drawn by an adult.
- ✓ The adult draws vertical lines for the child to copy.
- ✓ The child then draws horizontal lines for the child to copy.
- ✓ The adult draws a circle for the child to copy.
- ✓ Ensure the child is holding the crayon with their fingers.
- ✓ Also make sure they are holding the paper with their other hand.

Other tips

- A child that is just starting with circles might do circular scribble and this is ok initially.
- Work on copying vertical lines first and progress to horizontal lines and circles.
- Using larger paper is great for children who find drawing shapes difficult. This can include putting the paper on an easel.
- If the child is easily able to do those three shapes, they can also do a '+' and attempt a square.

Activity WS3:   Finger crayons and mazes

What you need   Finger crayons

Worksheets – mazes most suited for the child's age (see page 45 for details and below for targets)

Final target   For children under 5 years – the child can accurately trace within a 2cm wide single curved maze (Mazes 2-2), keeping their pencil inside the lines 80% of the time.

For children over 5 years – the child can accurately trace within a 1cm wide single curved maze (Mazes 3-2), keeping their pencil inside the lines 80% of the time.

For children over 6 years - the child can accurately trace within a 1cm wide multiple curved maze (Mazes 3-4), keeping their pencil inside the lines 80% of the time.

What to do

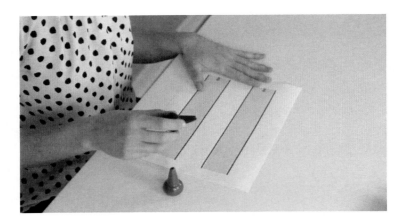

✓ Using the finger crayons, the child needs complete the maze worksheets.
✓ Start at the child's ability level and move through the maze worksheets until the child can complete the 1cm wide mazes accurately.
✓ Ensure the child is holding the crayon with their fingers.
✓ Also make sure they are holding the paper with their other hand.
✓ Ideally, the child should not lift their pencil off the paper until the maze is complete.

Other tips

• Ensure child doesn't turn the page as they are working.
• Encourage the child to leave their crayon on the paper as they complete the mazes.
• There are a large number of maze worksheets. Use the assessment pack to determine the best place for the child to start. Continue working on the mazes until the child can achieve the suggested target.

Activity WS4: Short pencils and shape colouring

What you need   Short pencils
Worksheets – Shapes 1, 2 or 3 depending on the child's ability.

Final target   The child can colour in 80% of a square and circle without going outside of the boundary lines more than 0.5 cm.

What to do

✓ The child uses the short pencils to colour in the shapes.
✓ Ensure the child is holding the pencils with their fingers. Ideally their little finger and ring finger will tuck away. You can also secure a piece of dowel into these fingers if that helps.
✓ Also, make sure they are holding the paper with their other hand.

Other tips

- There are three levels of worksheets here:
  - Shapes 1 – easy shapes with few edges and turns
  - Shapes 2 – harder shapes with many edges and turns
  - Shapes 3 – pictures – some children with a lower level of skill may be more motivated by colouring in the pictures initially, so these can be used to facilitate engagement, even if the child can't stay within the lines

Activity WS5:   Short pencils and lines

What you need   Short pencils
Blank paper – ideally large paper

Final target   The child will be able to complete the following pre-writing shapes:
- 4 year olds – | - o +
- 5 year olds – above shapes plus □ \ /
- 6 years plus – above shapes plus x Δ

What to do

✓ Using the short pencils, the child needs to copy the shapes as they are drawn by an adult.
✓ The adult draws the relevant shapes for the child's age, but can start with easier ones.
✓ Ensure the child is holding the pencil with their fingers.
✓ Also make sure they are holding the paper with their other hand.

Other tips

- If the child is easily able to do all of the shapes focus on their name and other letters of the alphabet.

Activity WS6: Short pencils and mazes or lines

What you need
Short pencils
Worksheets – Mazes or lines most suited for the child's age (see page 45 for details and below for targets)

Final target
For children under 5 years – the child can accurately trace within a 2cm wide multiple curved maze (Mazes 2-4), keeping their pencil inside the lines 80% of the time.

For 5 year olds – the child can accurately trace within a 1cm wide multiple curved maze (Mazes 3-4), keeping their pencil inside the lines 80% of the time.

For children over 6 years - the child can accurately trace within a 0.5cm wide multiple curved lined (Lines 1-3), keeping their pencil on the lines 80% of the time.

What to do

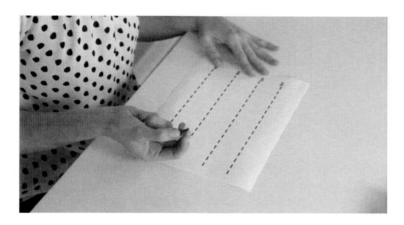

- ✓ The child needs to use short pencils to complete the maze and line worksheets.
- ✓ Start at the child's ability level and move through mazes until they can complete the suggested final target for their age.
- ✓ The child should not lift their pencil off the paper until the line is completed.
- ✓ Ensure the child is holding the pencils with their fingers. Ideally, their little finger and ring finger will tuck away. You can also secure a piece of dowel into these fingers if that helps.
- ✓ Also, make sure they are holding the paper with their other hand.

Other tips

- Ensure the child doesn't turn the paper sideways to help.
- Slowly work up the levels until the child can achieve accuracy with the target suggested for their age. The wider mazes are obviously easier than the lines and dotted lines.

Activity WS7:   Multiple direction lines

What you need   Regular pencils OR markers OR short pencils if required

Worksheets – lines with multiple directions (lines worksheets ending in -3 and -4).

Final target   For 5 year olds – the child can accurately trace along a thick dotted line which changes directions (Lines 2-3), keeping their pencil on the lines 80% of the time.

For 6 year olds – the child can accurately trace along a thin dotted line which changes directions (Lines 3-3), keeping their pencil on the lines 80% of the time.

For 7 year olds – the child can accurately trace along a thin dotted line which changes directions and crosses over itself (Lines 3-4), keeping their pencil on the lines 80% of the time.

What to do

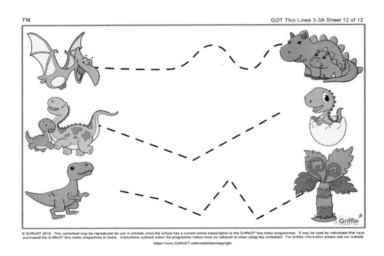

- ✓ The child needs to accurately complete the maze and line worksheets.
- ✓ Start at the child's ability level and move through until they can reach the suggested target.
- ✓ Ensure the child is holding the pencil with their fingers. Ideally, their little finger and ring finger will tuck away. You can also secure a piece of dowel into these fingers if that helps. Or if a child is really struggling they can continue to use short pencils.
- ✓ Also, make sure they are holding the paper with their other hand.
- ✓ Make sure the child doesn't turn the paper or lift their pencil off the page when completing a line.
- ✓ Focus on accuracy rather than speed.

Other tips

- • Ensure the child doesn't turn the paper sideways to help.
- • Slowly work up the levels until the child can achieve accuracy with the target suggested for their age.

Activity WS8: Zig zags

What you need Short pencils – if children are using all of their fingers on a pencil still

Regular pencils or markers

Worksheets – mazes and lines ending with -5

Final target For 5 year olds – the child can accurately trace within a 0.5cm wide zig zag line (Lines 1-5), keeping their pencil on the lines 80% of the time.

For children over 6 years - the child can accurately trace within a 0.2cm wide zig zag lined (Lines 2-5), keeping their pencil on the lines 80% of the time.

What to do

✓ The child needs to accurately complete the maze and line worksheets.

✓ Start at the child's ability level and move through until they can reach the suggested target.

✓ Ensure the child is holding the pencil with their fingers. Ideally, their little finger and ring finger will tuck away. You can also secure a piece of dowel into these fingers if that helps. Or if a child is really struggling they can continue to use short pencils.

✓ Also, make sure they are holding the paper with their other hand.

✓ Make sure the child doesn't turn the paper or lift their pencil off the page when completing a line.

✓ Focus on accuracy rather than speed.

Other tips

• Ensure the child doesn't turn the paper sideways to help.

• Slowly work up the levels until the child can achieve accuracy with the target suggested for their age. The wider mazes are easier than the lines and dotted lines. If the child can't complete the zig zag, try the multiple curve sheets as they help to practice the direction change required.

Activity WS9: Short pencils and hurricane circles

What you need   Short pencils
                      Paper

Final target   The child completes three looped circles using only finger movements (i.e. there is no movement at their shoulder, elbow or wrist).

What to do

- ✓ The child needs to use short pencils to draw hurricane shaped circles. Start at the middle and then draw around and around. Make sure the child moves their fingers only.
- ✓ Focus on accuracy rather than speed.
- ✓ Ensure the child is holding the pencil with their fingers. Ideally, their little finger and ring finger will tuck away. You can also secure a piece of dowel into these fingers if that helps.
- ✓ Also, make sure they are holding the paper with their other hand.

Other tips

- Many children find it difficult to just move their fingers and will move their wrists to create the movement. You may need to gently hold the child's wrist initially to help them to understand to move their fingers.

Activity WS10:   Dots in circles

What you need   Markers (pencils can be used but markers show up more easily)
Worksheets – GOTPG – WS10

Final target   The child can put a dot into each circle by using finger movements (i.e. there is no
movement at their shoulder, elbow or wrist).

What to do

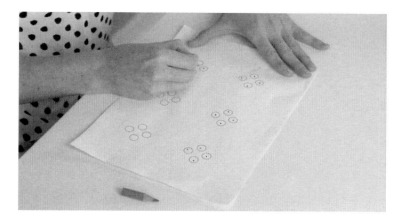

✓ The child places their hand on the paper. They make a dot into each circle in the set by moving their
fingers only.
✓ Focus on accuracy rather than speed.
✓ The child should be using a tripod, quadruped or modified tripod grasp. If they are not then they may
need a pencil grip.
✓ Ensure they are holding the paper with their non-dominant hand.

Other tips

• The child should not be moving their wrist or moving the pencil up and down in their fingers.
• You may need to gently hold the child's wrist initially to help them to understand to move their fingers.

Activity WS11:   Flowers

What you need   Pencils (markers can be used if needed)
Worksheets – GOTPG – WS11

Final target   The child can complete a flower moving around the lines without lifting their pencil and by moving only their fingers.

What to do

✓ The child places their hand on the paper. They move their pencil around the lines of the cross or star so they make a bump over each line.
✓ They should not lift their pencil until they have moved all of the way around the shape.
✓ Focus on accuracy rather than speed.
✓ The child should be using a tripod, quadruped or modified tripod grasp. If they are not then they may need a pencil grip. Small pencils can also be used.
✓ Ensure they are holding the paper with their non-dominant hand.

Other tips

• The child should not be moving their wrist or moving the pencil up and down in their fingers.

Activity WS12: Dot Patterns

What you need   Pencils
Worksheets – GOTPG – WS12

Final target   The child can accurately copy across diagonal and combined straight lines onto a 5x5 dot square. Touching each dot in the pattern and stopping on the last dot without overshooting.

What to do

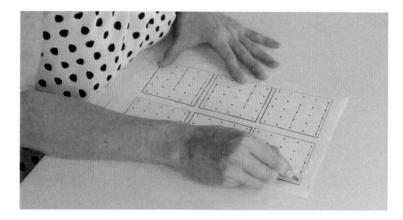

- ✓ The child needs to copy the pattern shown onto the blank set of dots.
- ✓ Make sure the child accurately stops at the end and that they touch each dot along the line. Focus on accuracy rather than speed.
- ✓ The child should be using a tripod, quadruped or modified tripod grasp. If they are not then they may need a pencil grip.
- ✓ Ensure they are holding the paper with their non-dominant hand.

Other tips

- For left handers, turn the page upside down so they can easily see the pattern they are copying (when it's the right way up their hand obscures the pattern).
- These sheets are again in levels. There are four different options: a 3x3 dot square for children that are finding it very hard; a 4x4 dot square as level 2; level 3 is 5x5 or the target. Choose the level that best suits the child's ability and work through them.

Activity WS13:   Infinity

What you need   Pencils (can be short or regular)
Paper or Worksheet – GOTPG – WS13 if needed

Final target   The child completes a figure 8 loop using finger movements only (i.e. there is no movement at their shoulder, elbow or wrist).

What to do

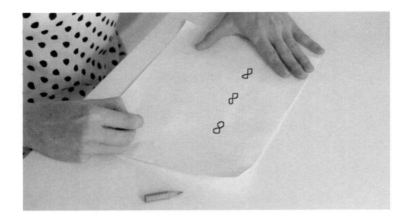

✓ The child needs to make an infinity sign. Start at middle and working around and back.
✓ Make sure they cross the loop in the middle rather than doing one side then doing the other.
✓ Make sure the child moves their fingers only.
✓ Focus on accuracy rather than speed.
✓ Ensure the child is holding the pencil with their fingers. Ideally, their little finger and ring finger will tuck away. You can also secure a piece of dowel into these fingers if that helps. Small pencils can also be used.
✓ Also, make sure they are holding the paper with their other hand.

Other tips

• Many children find this pattern very hard. Use the worksheet or draw it for them to trace over initially to help if this is the case.
• Ensure they keep their paper straight, rather than turning their paper to allow them to do an 8 instead of infinity. Some children will see perceptually that they can cheat using their strategy.
• However, if the child is really struggling, initially they could start with the number 8 (again make sure they cross over in the middle) and then progress to the infinity.

Activity WS14:   Loops

What you need   Pencils or short pencils
Paper or Worksheet – GOTPG – WS14 if needed

Final target   The child completes a figure 8 loop using finger movements only (i.e. there is no movement at their shoulder, elbow or wrist).

What to do

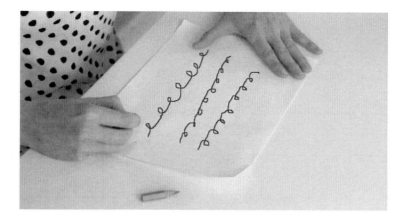

✓ The child needs to make an eeee loop.
✓ Make sure the child moves their fingers only to create the loop – their hand will move across the page as they go across however the fingers should be creating the loop.
✓ Make sure they cross over in the middle of the loop and come back.
✓ Once they have done the pattern facing upwards, have them try to turn it upside down.
✓ Focus on accuracy rather than speed.
✓ Ensure the child is holding the pencil with their fingers. Ideally, their little finger and ring finger will tuck away. You can also secure a piece of dowel into these fingers if that helps. Small pencils can also be used.
✓ Also, make sure they are holding the paper with their other hand.

Other tips

• Many children find it difficult to just move their fingers and will move their wrists to create the movement. You may need to gently hold the child's wrist initially to help them to understand to move their fingers.
• Again some children find this pattern very challenging. Use the worksheet or draw it for them to trace over initially to help if this is the case.
• The upside down version can be very hard for some children, so don't worry if it takes them a while.
• If the child can manage both directions easily you can join them together into an fffff pattern. So, the child draws one facing upwards then one facing downwards.

Pencil Grip Pre & Review Assessment

Child Name:

Pre assessment date: Completed by:

Review assessment date 1:   Completed by:

Review assessment date 2:   Completed by:

1. How does the child currently hold their pencil?

	Pre-Assessment	Review 1	Review 2
Gross Grasp or Palmer Grasp			
Digital Pronate			
Static Tripod			
Dynamic Tripod			
Static Quadruped			
Dynamic Quadruped			
Modified Tripod			
Fingers Along the Shaft			
Thumb Wrap			
Lateral Grasp			
Other (describe)			

2. Which shapes can the child copy (i.e. draw if you give them a picture of it)?

	Pre-Assessment	Review 1	Review 2
Vertical Line |			
Horizontal Line –			
Circle o			
Straight Cross +			
Oblique Line /			
Square			
Oblique Line \			
Oblique Cross x			
Triangle			

Pencil Grip Pre & Review Assessment (continued)

3. How many letters of the alphabet can the child complete with correct formations?

Pre-Assessment	Review 1	Review 2

4. What is the highest level of worksheet the child is able to complete with 80% accuracy?

Pre-Assessment	Review 1	Review 2

5. Have the child write their name:

Pre-Assessment	
Review 1	
Review 2	

5. Have the child draw a person:

Pre-Assessment	Review Date

Please note there is a reproducible copy of this form available for download on the GriffinOT website, see page 63 for details.

Group Record Sheet

Date: List: Staff members:

Child's Name or Initials	Activity			

Please note there is a reproducible copy of this form available for download on the GriffinOT website, see page 63 for details.

References

1. Beery, K.E., Beery, N.A. (2010) *The Beery-Buktenica developmental test of Visual Motor Integration. Sixth Edition.* Pearson, MN.
2. Dornan, G. (2010). *Tips for Teaching: Writing Grip.* National Handwriting Association UK.
3. Dornan, G. (2017). *Tips for Teaching: 'P' Checks.* National Handwriting Association UK.
4. Sheridan, M.D. (2008) *From Birth to Five Years. Children's Developmental Progress. Third Edition.* Routledge, London.

Extra Resources

On our website, GriffinOT.com, you will find the additional resources required to run this programme. These include:

- Downloadable copies of all worksheets
- Link to *Crocodile Snap* music and video
- Downloadable copies of assessment and record sheets
- Worksheet assessment packs
- Videos demonstrating the various grasps described in early chapters of the book
- Video demonstrating how to make a resistance ball
- Links to GriffinOT videos reviewing pencil grips
- Discounted access to the online training manual

To access these resources please go to www.GriffinOT.com/SPGD. You will need the password **G1raff341#** to access this page. This password is case sensitive with a hashtag at the end. Please do not share this password with others who do not own a copy of this book. Without purchase of the book, users are breaching copyright by accessing the materials.

To complement this book there is online training manual. The online manual includes educational videos on the topics in the book, and extra information on posture. There are video demonstrations of how to do all of the activities in the book. A set of 400 extra worksheets is also available. Anyone who has purchased this book can access this training at a reduced cost. Details are on the resource page above.

You can also stay in touch by following us on social media.

Twitter: @Griffin_OT

Facebook: www.Facebook.com/GriffinSensoryOT/

You can also join the mailing list to keep up to date with any changes in our resources. You can join the mailing list on our website.

Website: www.GriffinOT.com

Also by GriffinOT

Fine Motor Skills – Launching September 2019

The GriffinOT Fine Motor Skills Programme (FMSP) is an online resource which includes of over 120 activities designed to help children from age 3 ½ and above improve their fine motor skills. Fine motor skills are the small movements our hands and fingers make during fine motor activities. Doing up buttons, squeezing toothpaste onto a toothbrush, cutting with scissors and using a pencil are examples of fine motor activities. In fact, any activity that you do with your hands and fingers relies on your fine motor skills.

The FMSP is broken into four developmental levels. Each level supports sequential development of fine motor skills, such as finger and hand control, using both hands together, hand strength and accuracy. For each activity in the programme there is an instructional video. This shows the adult what the child should be doing when they complete the activity. It also shows how the child should not do the activity, i.e. the cheats they should avoid and how to make the activity harder or easier if required. In addition, each level of the programme includes educational videos related to the skills that the child is developing.

Sensory Processing: What's the Fuss? – Online Now

The online course, 'Sensory Processing – What's the Fuss?' provides an introduction to Sensory Processing Disorder (SPD) for parents and teachers. The course covers the seven senses, the elements of SPD and how to help to support children or adults that have sensory processing challenges. It includes 4.5 hours of video and additional resources to support learning. Like all of our products, the course aims to teach you not just what to do but how to use sensory strategies correctly and safely.

Sensory Group Book 1 – Available Now

Sensory Group Book 1 is a 12-24 week programme for children who need extra support to engage in sensory-based play. This includes children who avoid messy textures or noisy toys and children who just might not notice sensory-play opportunities. The programme targets children's auditory, visual, touch and proprioceptive senses. It is progressive, with each list building on the previous one, to increase children's engagement with sensory-play activities over time. The group aims to target not only sensory sensitivity and avoidance, but also joint attention and turn taking.

Developing Children's Scissor Skills – Coming early 2020

Scissor Skill Development is part of GriffinOT's fine motor skill programme. Just like Supporting Pencil Grasp Development, there will be step by step activities to help to improve a child's ability to use scissors. There will be activities and worksheets within the book and other tips to help children to be successful with their scissor skills.

Gross Motor Skills – Coming in 2021

To complement and support our fine motor skill development programme, GriffinOT plans to release a gross motor skill development programme in 2021. Join our mailing list, or follow us on social media, to be the first to hear when this is available.

You can find out more about all of our resources on our website www.GriffinOT.com. Thank you for your purchase and we hope you have found our resources helpful.